Printed and bound for Ravette Books Limited
8 Clifford Street, London W1X 1RB
An Egmont Company
by New Interlitho S.p.A., Milan

ISBN : 1 85304 592 6

THE GARFIELD BIRTHDAY BOOK

JIM DAVIS

ЯR

RAVETTE BOOKS

Contents

7

IN TWO DAYS I'LL BE TWO YEARS OLD... THAT'S FOURTEEN YEARS IN HUMAN TERMS

6-17

I CAN'T WAIT

IN ANOTHER FOUR MONTHS I'LL BE OLD ENOUGH TO DRIVE

JIM DAVIS   © 1980 United Feature Syndicate, Inc.

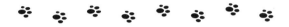

TOMORROW I'LL BE TWO YEARS OF AGE. THAT'S THE HUMAN EQUIVALENT OF FOURTEEN

6-18

CATS HAVE IT GOOD

ADOLESCENCE WITHOUT ACNE

JIM DAVIS   © 1980 United Feature Syndicate, Inc.

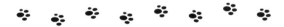

TODAY IS MY BIRTHDAY, AND I HATE BIRTHDAYS. I'M GOING TO GET A SURPRISE PARTY, AND I HATE SURPRISE PARTIES

JIM DAVIS   © 1980 United Feature Syndicate, Inc.

SURPRISE, GARFIELD!

BUT I LOOOOOVE THE ATTENTION!

6-19

8

9

Another year gone by, and
I haven't changed a bit . . .

Well, there's always next year!

Let's Party

Some suggestions for party games

The Mating Call Game

This is an excellent game to get a party going. All the women are asked to go to one end of the room and put on blindfolds. They are told that their partners will call them and then, individually, each one is given an animal name such as a sheep, a pig, a horse etc. Meanwhile, at the other end of the room, the men are told they are looking for a mate and must call them using the noises made by the animals. When the game is ready to begin, the women are turned round a couple of times to confuse their sense of direction and the men start to baa, grunt and whinney etc. as loudly as they can. The result is a hilarious din in which the partners try to find each other. The winner, of course, is the pair that gets together first.

(If you are coping with large numbers, you may run out of common animal noises. So you can always add bird calls or mechanical noises like a car horn or both.)

The Instant Laughter Game

This is another noisy game which is good for breaking the ice at a party. The guests are divided into two groups of equal size and have to line up opposite each other. Someone is picked to be Controller of Laughter and he or she stands in the middle between the two lines. The Controller has an old hat which he throws into the air. If it lands the right way up, team 1 has to laugh loudly and convincingly while team 2 remains silent. If the hat lands upside-down, team 2 have to laugh while team 1 remains silent. Anyone from either side who fails to respond in the correct way (or doesn't laugh well enough) is transferred to the opposite team by the Controller. The winning team is the one that captures all its opposite members or has the greater number of people in it at the end of a given time.

(A simpler variant of this game is for everyone to stand in a circle with the Controller in the middle. He or she has a handkerchief which is thrown into the air. At this signal, everyone must start to laugh loudly. When the hanky touches the ground or is caught by the Controller, they must stop. Anyone who fails to do either of these things is eliminated.)

The Love Letter Game

This game needs a bit of preparation, but it is a sure-fire winner. You need some sheets of plain paper, scissors, paper glue and some old magazines. When the game starts, divide your guests into groups of about four or five and give each group the paper etc. The idea of the game is to make up a love letter using only the materials provided – nothing must be written in pen. So the guests have to find words or phrases in the magazines, cut them out and stick them on the paper to make a coherent letter. This causes great laughter and at the end of a set period (say 20 minutes), each group can read out its finished letter to the others.

Consequences

An old favourite, this one, but a game that always has everyone falling about with laughter. Paper and pen are all you need. One person is chosen as caller and everyone else is given a piece of paper and a pen. The caller begins the story and everyone writes down the name of someone in the group or a famous person. Then everybody folds down the top of the paper to hide what has been written and passes it on to the next person. The caller makes a second call, another name is written down and the folding/passing takes place again. This process goes on until the story is finished. The pieces of paper are then read out. The traditional stages of the story are:

1. A girl
2. Met a boy
3. In/at/beside
4. He said
5. She said
6. The consequence was
7. And the world said

Scavenger Hunt

This indoor form of treasure hunt can be played by both adults and children. To prepare, you have to make a list of articles that have to be found and duplicate it. The list can be as long or as short as you wish and can include anything from the sublime to the ridiculous (provided you know it can be found in your house or garden!) Your guests are divided into pairs and each given a list and a time-limit (say 30 minutes) in which to find every item on the list. Everyone rushes off to collect the things like scavengers plundering the countryside. The winner is the first pair to find everything, or whoever gets the most items when the time-limit expires.

Here's a possible list for a normal suburban household: magazine or comic. . . coin. . . item of clothing like sock or tie. . . kitchen equipment like spoon or saucepan. . . book. . . blade of grass or leaf from tree or both. . . jam-jar label. . . small item from garage like nut or bolt. . . signature of neighbour or passer-by. . . flower.

(For a really exciting version of this game, you can organise a scavenger hunt in your road or area to be completed on foot or by bike.)

The Garfield Birthday Quiz

1. Who, according to the old Scottish song, was 'the lad born to be king'?

a) Macbeth
b) Bonnie Prince Charlie
c) Elvis Presley

2. The Queen of England's official birthday is a variable date in June. When is her *real* birthday?

a) April 21st
b) August 20th
c) November 22nd

3. In the film 'Born Free', what was the name of Joy Adamson's lion?

a) Eliza
b) Ailsa
c) Elsa

4. The exact date of William Shakespeare's birthday is not known.

a) True?
b) False?

5. Which actor was 'Born On The Fourth Of July'?

6. Which singer was 'Born In The USA'?

7. Who was the world's first test-tube baby, born on July 25th, 1978?

a) Louise Brown
b) Amanda White
c) Susanna Green

8. Ralph and Carolyn Cummings, from Virginia USA, had five children during the period 1952-1966 and they were *all* born on the same day of the year – February 20th.

a) True?
b) False?

9. Sharks are at their most vulnerable when they are first born because they are blind and have no teeth.

a) True?
b) False?

10. In the musical film 'Paint Your Wagon', which gravelly-voiced actor sang about being 'Born Under A Wandering Star'?

a) Lee Marvin
b) Hank Marvin
c) Marvin Gaye

11. The world's most frequently sung song was written by two American Sunday School teachers, Mildred Hill and Patty Smith Hill, in 1893. What is it called?

12. According to 'Garfield – His Nine Lives', where *exactly* was Garfield born?

Answers

7. a) Louise Brown
6. Bruce Springsteen
5. Tom Cruise
4. a) True
3. c) Elsa
2. a) April 21st
1. b) Bonnie Prince Charlie

8. a) True
9. b) False (They are born perfectly formed and swim off to find their first meal)
10. a) Lee Marvin
11. 'Happy Birthday To You.'
12. In Mama Leone's Italian restaurant

17

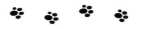

SURPRISE!

HAPPY BIRTHDAY, GARFIELD!

I HAD A FEELING THIS WAS COMING

GOOD HEAVENS! I'M GOING TO BE EIGHT YEARS OLD THIS THURSDAY!

JUNE

I HATE BIRTHDAYS. THEY'RE A LOT LIKE CALENDARS

JUNE

THEY REMIND YOU YOUR DAYS ARE NUMBERED

JUNE

I HAVE SOME BAD NEWS ABOUT YOUR BIRTHDAY CAKE, GARFIELD

IT COLLAPSED UNDER THE WEIGHT OF THE CANDLES

IS THAT AN AGE JOKE?

OH WELL, IT WOULD PROBABLY HAVE SET OFF THE SMOKE ALARM ANYWAY

TIME-OUT! UNFAIR! AGE JOKE!

20

The Garfield Birthday Planner

(Don't forget Aunty Whatsername!)

January

1

2

3

4

5

6

7

8

9

10

11

12

13

14

15

16

17

18

19	
20	
21	
22	
23	
24	
25	
26	
27	
28	
29	
30	
31	

February

1
2
3
4
5
6
7
8
9
10
11
12
13
14
15
16
17
18

19	
20	
21	
22	
23	
24	
25	
26	
27	
28	
(29)	

March

1

2

3

4

5

6

7

8

9

10

11

12

13

14

15

16

17

18

19	
20	
21	
22	
23	
24	
25	
26	
27	
28	
29	
30	
31	

April

1

2

3

4

5

6

7

8

9

10

11

12

13

14

15

16

17

18

19	
20	
21	
22	
23	
24	
25	
26	
27	
28	
29	
30	

May

1
2
3
4
5
6
7
8
9
10
11
12
13
14
15
16
17
18

19	
20	
21	
22	
23	
24	
25	
26	
27	
28	
29	
30	
31	

June

1
2
3
4
5
6
7
8
9
10
11
12
13
14
15
16
17
18

19	
20	
21	
22	
23	
24	
25	
26	
27	
28	
29	
30	

July

1
2
3
4
5
6
7
8
9
10
11
12
13
14
15
16
17
18

19	
20	
21	
22	
23	
24	
25	
26	
27	
28	
29	
30	
31	

August

1

2

3

4

5

6

7

8

9

10

11

12

13

14

15

16

17

18

19

20

21

22

23

24

25

26

27

28

29

30

31

September

1
2
3
4
5
6
7
8
9
10
11
12
13
14
15
16
17
18

19	
20	
21	
22	
23	
24	
25	
26	
27	
28	
29	
30	

October

1
2
3
4
5
6
7
8
9
10
11
12
13
14
15
16
17
18

19
20
21
22
23
24
25
26
27
28
29
30
31

November

1
2
3
4
5
6
7
8
9
10
11
12
13
14
15
16
17
18

19	
20	
21	
22	
23	
24	
25	
26	
27	
28	
29	
30	

December

1
2
3
4
5
6
7
8
9
10
11
12
13
14
15
16
17
18

19

20

21

22

23

24

25

26

27

28

29

30

31

Here's something for a cat who has everything –

A slave dog!

HAPPY BIRTHDAY, GARFIELD! WE LOVE YOU!

JIM DAVIS 6-19

DO YOU KNOW THE BEST PART OF BIRTHDAYS?

FOR A DAY, IT'S NICE TO HAVE THE WORLD REVOLVE AROUND YOU!

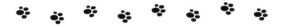

HAPPY BIRTHDAY, GARFIELD. HERE'S A DOUBLE-CHOCOLATE FUDGE MARSHMALLOW CREAM CAKE!

JIM DAVIS 6-20

AND HERE'S CHOCOLATE CHIP ICE CREAM, SUGAR COOKIES AND A CHERRY PHOSPHATE! ANY QUESTIONS?

YEH...

WHAT'S FOR DESSERT?

FOR YOUR BIRTHDAY I GOT YOU A DIET BOOK

GEE, THANKS! THIS IS PERFECT!

JIM DAVIS 6-21

47

HEY, GARFIELD, YOU'RE GOING TO BE NINE YEARS OLD THIS FRIDAY

THANKS FOR REMINDING ME

AS CATS GO, YOU'RE APPROACHING THE GOLDEN YEARS

THE HECK WITH THE GOLDEN YEARS. I'M FIVE AND HOLDING

6-17

JIM DAVIS

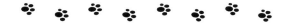

WHAT'S THE MATTER, GARFIELD? FEELING YOUR YEARS NOW THAT YOU'RE TURNING NINE?

COME CLOSER, MY SON. I'M HAVING TROUBLE HEARING YOU

6-18

SLAP! SLAP! SLAP! SLAP!

HAPPY BIRTHDAY, GARFIELD!!

THAT SURE IS A LOT OF CANDLES

OH WELL, I SHOULD BE HAPPY TO HAVE A BIRTHDAY, I GUESS

FFFFF

AS OPPOSED TO THE ALTERNATIVE

JIM DAVIS 6-19

48

Life is a lot like a hot bath – it feels good while you're in it. . .

But the longer you stay, the more wrinkled you get!

Whose Birthday is it, anyway?

**Find out which famous person
shares *your* birthday. . .**

January

1. E.M. Forster (1879)
   Novelist
2. David Bailey (1938)
   Photographer
3. Marcus Tullius Cicero (106BC)
   Roman statesman
4. Louis Braille (1809)
   Inventor of reading system for the blind
5. Diane Keaton (1946)
   Actress
6. Joan of Arc (1412)
   French soldier and heroine
7. Gerald Durrell (1925)
   Naturalist and writer
8. Elvis Presley (1935)
   Rock 'n' roll singer
9. Joan Baez (1941)
   Folk singer
10. Rod Stewart (1945)
    Pop singer
11. Alan Paton (1903)
    South African writer
12. Jack London (1876)
    Novelist
13. Sophie Tucker (1884)
    American musical star
14. Faye Dunaway (1941)
    Actress
15. Martin Luther King (1929)
    Civil Rights Leader
16. Andre Michelin (1853)
    Inventor of rubber tyres
17. Benjamin Franklin (1706)
    American statesman and scientist
18. Danny Kaye (1913)
    Actor and comedian
19. Edgar Allan Poe (1809)
    Writer of horror stories
20. George Burns (1896)
    Comedian
21. Telly Savalas (1925)
    Actor
22. Lord Byron (1788)
    English poet
23. Edouard Manet (1832)
    French painter
24. Hadrian (76 AD)
    Roman emperor who built the wall
25. Robert Burns (1759)
    Scottish poet
26. Paul Newman (1925)
    Actor
27. Wolfgang Amadeus Mozart (1756)
    Composer
28. Alan Alda (1936)
    Actor
29. W.C. Fields (1879)
    Comedy actor
30. Gene Hackman (1931)
    Actor
31. Phil Collins (1951)
    Singer / Songwriter

February

1. Clark Gable (1901)
   Actor
2. James Joyce (1882)
   Irish writer
3. Felix Mendelssohn (1809)
   Composer
4. Charles Lindbergh (1902)
   Pioneer aviator
5. Bob Marley (1945)
   Reggae singer
6. Christopher Marlowe (1664)
   English dramatist
7. Charles Dickens (1812)
   Novelist
8. James Dean (1931)
   Actor and cult idol
9. Mia Farrow (1945)
   Actress
10. Boris Pasternak (1890)
    Russian novelist ('Dr Zhivago')
11. Burt Reynolds (1936)
    Actor
12. Charles Darwin (1809)
    Naturalist
13. Georges Simenon (1903)
    Novelist, creator of Maigret
14. Thomas Malthus (1766)
    Pioneer economist
15. Galileo Galilei (1564)
    Astronomer
16. John McEnroe (1959)
    Tennis player
17. Barry Humphries (1934)
    Creator of Dame Edna Everidge
18. John Travolta (1954)
    Dancer and actor
19. Nicolaus Copernicus (1473)
    Astronomer
20. Sidney Poitier (1927)
    Actor
21. W.H. Auden (1907)
    English poet
22. George Washington (1732)
    First American president
23. Samuel Pepys (1633)
    Writer of the world-famous diary
24. Alain Prost (1955)
    Racing driver
25. Pierre-Auguste Renoir (1841)
    French painter
26. Johnny Cash (1932)
    Country and western singer
27. Elizabeth Taylor (1932)
    Actress
28. Charles Blondin (1824)
    French tightrope walker (who crossed Niagara Falls)
29. Gioacchino Rossini (1792)
    Composer

March

1. Glenn Miller (1904)
   American bandleader
2. Naomi James (1949)
   Lone round-the-world yachtswoman
3. Alexander Graham Bell (1847)
   Inventor of the telephone
4. Antonio Vivaldi (1678)
   Composer
5. Rex Harrison (1905)
   Actor
6. Ronald Reagan (1911)
   Actor and American president
7. Ivan Lendl (1960)
   Tennis player
8. Kenneth Grahame (1859)
   Author ('Wind In The Willows')
9. Amerigo Vespucci (1454)
   Explorer who gave his name to America
10. Bix Beiderbecke (1903)
    American jazz musician
11. Malcolm Campbell (1885)
    Holder of speed records on land and sea
12. Liza Minnelli (1946)
    Actress and singer
13. Neil Sedaka (1939)
    Singer / Songwriter
14. Michael Caine (1933)
    Actor
15. Mike Love (1941)
    Founding member of the Beach Boys
16. Jerry Lewis (1926)
    Zany film comedian
17. Nat 'King' Cole (1917)
    Singer
18. Wilfred Owen (1893)
    World War 1 poet
19. David Livingstone (1813)
    Explorer and missionary
20. Ovid (43 BC)
    Roman poet
21. J.S. Bach (1685)
    Composer
22. Marcel Marceau (1923)
    French mime artist
23. Joan Crawford (1908)
    Actress
24. Steve McQueen (1930)
    Actor
25. Elton John (1947)
    Singer / Songwriter
26. Diana Ross (1944)
    Singer
27. Sir Henry Royce (1863)
    Co-founder (with Arthur Rolls) of Rolls-Royce
28. Raphael (1483)
    Italian painter
29. William Walton (1902)
    English composer
30. Eric Clapton (1945)
    Rock guitarist
31. Richard Chamberlain (1935)
    Actor

April

1. William Harvey (1578)
   Physician who discovered blood circulation
2. Hans Christian Andersen (1803)
   Writer of fairy tales
3. Marlon Brando (1924)
   Actor
4. Muddy Waters (1915)
   Blues singer
5. Gregory Peck (1916)
   Actor
6. Harry Houdini (1874)
   Escape artist
7. David Frost (1939)
   TV presenter and producer
8. Mary Pickford (1893)
   Actress (in early films)
9. Paul Robeson (1898)
   Actor and singer
10. Omar Sharif (1932)
    Actor
11. Popeye (1929)
    Cartoon character (first appearance in newspaper)
12. Maria Callas (1923)
    Opera singer
13. Samuel Beckett (1906)
    Irish playwright
14. Julie Christie (1940)
    Actress
15. Henry James (1843)
    American novelist
16. Charlie Chaplin (1889)
    Actor and comedian
17. James Last (1929)
    Bandleader
18. Hayley Mills (1946)
    Actress and child star
19. Dudley Moore (1935)
    Comedian and musician
20. Ryan O'Neal (1941)
    Actor
21. Charlotte Bronte (1816)
    Novelist ('Jane Eyre')
22. Yehudi Menuhin (1916)
    Violinist
23. Roy Orbison (1936)
    Singer
24. Barbra Streisand (1942)
    Singer and actress
25. Oliver Cromwell (1559)
    English soldier and statesman
26. Leonardo da Vinci (1452)
    Painter and man of genius
27. Samuel Morse (1791)
    Inventor of morse code
28. Charles Sturt (1795)
    Explorer of Australia
29. Duke Ellington (1889)
    Jazz musician
30. Franz Lehar (1870)
    Composer

May

1. Rita Coolidge (1945)
   Singer
2. Bing Crosby (1904)
   Singer and actor
3. Pete Seeger (1919)
   Folk singer
4. Audrey Hepburn (1929)
   Actress
5. Karl Marx (1818)
   Economist and philosopher
6. Orson Welles (1915)
   Actor and director
7. Pyotr Ilich Tchaikovsky (1840)
   Composer
8. Peter Benchley (1940)
   Novelist ('Jaws')
9. J.M. Barrie (1860)
   Author, creator of Peter Pan
10. Fred Astaire (1899)
    Dancer and actor
11. Salvador Dali (1904)
    Surrealist painter
12. Florence Nightingale (1820)
    Nurse
13. Daphne du Maurier (1907)
    Novelist
14. Thomas Gainsborough (1727)
    Portrait painter
15. Frank Baum (1856)
    Author, creator of the Wizard of Oz
16. Liberace (1919)
    Pianist and showman
17. Erik Satie (1866)
    French composer
18. Margot Fonteyn (1919)
    Ballerina
19. Nellie Melba (1848)
    Opera singer
20. Cher (1945)
    Singer and actress
21. 'Fats' Waller (1904)
    Jazz pianist
22. Arthur Conan Doyle (1859)
    Novelist, creator of Sherlock Holmes
23. Joan Collins (1933)
    Actress
24. Bob Dylan (1941)
    Singer/Songwriter
25. Gene Tunney (1898)
    Heavyweight boxing champion
26. John Wayne (1907)
    Actor
27. 'Wild Bill' Hickok (1837)
    Cowboy and U.S. Marshall
28. Ian Fleming (1908)
    Novelist, creator of James Bond
29. John F. Kennedy (1917)
    American President
30. Mel Blanc (1908)
    The voice of Bugs Bunny (and others)
31. Clint Eastwood (1930)
    Actor

June

1. Marilyn Monroe (1926)
   Actress
2. Thomas Hardy (1840)
   Novelist
3. Tony Curtis (1925)
   Actor
4. Stephen Foster (1826)
   American songwriter ('Swanee River')
5. John Couch Adams (1819)
   Astronomer who discovered planet Neptune
6. Bjorn Borg (1956)
   Tennis champion
7. Paul Gauguin (1848)
   Painter
8. Nancy Sinatra (1940)
   Singer (daughter of Frank)
9. Cole Porter (1893)
   Composer of musicals
10. Judy Garland (1922)
    Singer and actress
11. Jacques Cousteau (1910)
    Underwater explorer
12. Anne Frank (1929)
    Dutch schoolgirl who wrote diary whilst in hiding from Nazis
13. W.B. Yeats (1865)
    Irish poet
14. Steffi Graf (1969)
    Tennis champion
15. Edvard Grieg (1843)
    Norwegian composer
16. Stan Laurel (1890)
    English-born half of comedy duo, Laurel and Hardy
17. Barry Manilow (1946)
    Singer/Songwriter
18. Paul McCartney (1942)
    Ex-Beatle and pop musician
19. GARFIELD (1978)
    (First appearance in American newspapers)
20. Catherine Cookson (1906)
    Historical novelist
21. Jean-Paul Sartre (1905)
    French writer and philosopher
22. Meryl Streep (1949)
    Actress
23. Empress Josephine (1763)
    Wife of Napoleon Bonaparte
24. Fred Hoyle (1915)
    Astronomer and science fiction writer
25. George Orwell (1903)
    Novelist
26. Mick Jagger (1943)
    Lead singer of the Rolling Stones
27. Helen Keller (1880)
    Blind, deaf and dumb teacher and writer
28. Mel Brooks (1926)
    Comedy actor/director
29. Antoine de Saint-Exupery (1900)
    French novelist and aviator
30. John Gay (1685)
    English poet and playwright ('The Beggar's Opera')

July

1. Carl Lewis (1961)
   Champion sprinter
2. Thomas Cranmer (1489)
   Archbishop to King Henry VIII
3. Ken Russell (1927)
   Film director
4. Louis Armstrong (1900)
   Jazz trumpeter
5. Phineas Barnum (1810)
   American showman
6. Sylvester Stallone (1946)
   Actor
7. Gustav Mahler (1860)
   Composer
8. Count von Zeppelin (1838)
   *Designer and manufacturer
   of airships*
9. Barbara Cartland (1901)
   Romantic novelist
10. Marcel Proust (1871)
    French novelist
11. Yul Brynner (1915)
    Actor
12. Julius Caesar (100BC)
    Roman soldier and statesman
13. Harrison Ford (1942)
    Actor
14. Woody Guthrie (1912)
    Folk singer / songwriter
15. Harmenszoon van Rijn
    Rembrandt (1606)
    Dutch painter
16. Roald Amundsen (1872)
    *Norwegian explorer, first to reach
    S. Pole*
17. James Cagney (1899)
    Actor
18. W.G. Grace (1848)
    English cricketer
19. Samuel Colt (1814)
    Inventor of six-shooter pistol
20. Edmund Hillary (1919)
    *Mountaineer, first to climb
    Mt. Everest*
21. Ernest Hemingway (1899)
    Novelist
22. Gregor Mendel (1822)
    *Botanist who formulated
    laws of genetic inheritance*
23. Raymond Chandler (1888)
    Crime novelist
24. Alexandre Dumas (1802)
    *French novelist
    ('Three Musketeers')*
25. Walter Brennan (1894)
    American character actor
26. George Bernard Shaw (1856)
    Irish writer
27. Christopher Dean (1958)
    *Ice-dance champion
    (with Jayne Torvill)*
28. JIM DAVIS (1945)
    Cartoonist
29. Benito Mussolini (1883)
    Italian Dictator
30. Emily Bronte (1818)
    Novelist ('Wuthering Heights')
31. Geraldine Chaplin (1944)
    Actress (daughter of Charlie)

August

1. Claudius (19BC)
   *Roman emperor who
   invaded Britain*
2. Peter O'Toole (1932)
   Actor
3. Martin Sheen (1940)
   Actor
4. Percy Bysshe Shelley (1792)
   Poet
5. Neil Armstrong (1930)
   Astronaut, first man on moon
6. Alexander Fleming (1881)
   *Scientist who
   discovered penicillin*
7. Louis Leakey (1903)
   *Archaeologist who studied early
   man in Africa*
8. Nigel Mansell (1954)
   Racing driver
9. Thomas Telford (1757)
   Scottish bridge engineer
10. Herbert Hoover (1874)
    *American president during
    the Depression*
11. Enid Blyton (1897)
    Children's author
12. Cecil B. De Mille (1881)
    Film director
13. Alfred Hitchcock (1899)
    Film director
14. John Galsworthy (1864)
    Novelist ('The Forsyte Saga')
15. Napoleon Bonaparte (1769)
    Emperor of France
16. Madonna (1958)
    Pop singer and actress
17. Davy Crockett (1786)
    American frontiersman
18. Robert Redford (1937)
    Actor
19. Coco Chanel (1883)
    Fashion designer
20. Jim Reeves (1924)
    Country and western singer
21. 'Count' Basie (1904)
    Jazz pianist and bandleader
22. Steve Davis (1957)
    Snooker champion
23. Gene Kelly (1912)
    *Dancer and actor
    ('Singing in the rain')*
24. William Wilberforce (1759)
    Anti-slave trade campaigner
25. Ivan the Terrible (1530)
    Russian Tsar
26. Joseph Montgolfier (1740)
    Pioneer hot air balloonist
27. Mother Teresa (1910)
    *Missionary nun in
    India (Calcutta)*
28. Leo Tolstoy (1828)
    Russian novelist
29. Michael Jackson (1958)
    Singer
30. Jean-Claude Killy (1943)
    French ski champion
31. Caligula (12 AD)
    Roman emperor

September

1. Edgar Rice Burroughs (1875)
   Novelist, creator of Tarzan
2. Jimmy Connors (1952)
   Tennis champion
3. Alan Ladd (1913)
   Actor
4. Tom Watson (1949)
   Golfer
5. Jesse James (1847)
   American outlaw
6. Joseph Kennedy (1888)
   *American politician, father of the
   Kennedy dynasty*
7. Buddy Holly (1936)
   Pop singer
8. Peter Sellers (1925)
   Comedy actor
9. Cardinal de Richelieu (1585)
   Powerful French statesman
10. Arnold Palmer (1929)
    Golfer
11. D.H. Lawrence (1885)
    Novelist
12. Maurice Chevalier (1888)
    French entertainer
13. Roald Dahl (1916)
    *Author, especially of
    children's books*
14. Baron von Humboldt (1769)
    *German explorer who invented
    the study of ecology*
15. Agatha Christie (1890)
    Crime writer
16. Henry V (1387)
    *English King at the
    Battle of Agincourt*
17. Anne Bancroft (1931)
    Actress
18. Greta Garbo (1905)
    Actress
19. Jeremy Irons (1948)
    Actor
20. Sophia Loren (1934)
    Actress
21. H.G. Wells (1866)
    Science fiction writer
22. Michael Faraday (1791)
    *Scientist who did pioneering
    work on electricity*
23. Bruce Springsteen (1949)
    Rock singer
24. F. Scott Fitzgerald (1896)
    Novelist
25. Christopher Reeve (1952)
    Actor (Superman)
26. Olivia Newton-John (1948)
    Singer and actress
27. George Cruikshank (1792)
    Political cartoonist
28. Brigitte Bardot (1934)
    Actress
29. Horatio Nelson (1758)
    British naval commander
30. Johnny Mathis (1935)
    Singer

54

October

1. Jimmy Carter (1924)
   American president
2. Mohandas K. Ghandi (1869)
   Indian leader
3. Chubby Checker (1941)
   Singer ('The Twist')
4. Buster Keaton (1895)
   Actor (early silent films)
5. Bob Geldof (1954)
   Singer and organiser of Live Aid
6. Thor Heyerdahl (1914)
   Norwegian scientist who crossed Pacific on Kon-Tiki balsa raft
7. Jayne Torvill (1957)
   Ice-dance champion (with Christopher Dean)
8. Rev. Jesse Jackson (1941)
   American politician
9. John Lennon (1940)
   Ex-Beatle and singer/songwriter
10. Giuseppe Verdi (1813)
    Opera composer
11. Francois Mauriac (1885)
    French novelist
12. Luciano Pavarotti (1935)
    Opera singer
13. Paul Simon (1941)
    Singer/songwriter
14. Cliff Richard (1940)
    Singer
15. Virgil (70BC)
    Roman epic poet
16. Oscar Wilde (1854)
    Writer and wit
17. Evel Knievel (1939)
    Stuntman
18. Martina Navratilova (1956)
    Tennis champion
19. John Le Carré (1931)
    Spy novelist
20. Christopher Wren (1632)
    Architect who built St Paul's Cathedral in London
21. Alfred Nobel (1833)
    Inventor of dynamite and founder of Peace Prize
22. Franz Liszt (1811)
    Composer
23. Pele (1940)
    Soccer player
24. Antonie van Leeuwenhoek (1632)
    Developer of microscope and first to see bacteria
25. Pablo Picasso (1881)
    Painter
26. François Mitterand (1919)
    French president
27. Captain Cook (1728)
    Explorer who discovered Australia and New Zealand
28. Evelyn Waugh (1903)
    Novelist
29. Richard Dreyfus (1949)
    Actor
30. John Adams (1735)
    Second American president
31. John Keats (1795)
    English poet

November

1. L.S. Lowry (1887)
   English painter
2. Daniel Boone (1734)
   American frontiersman and hunter
3. Charles Bronson (1921)
   Actor
4. Walter Cronkite (1916)
   American journalist and newscaster
5. Art Garfunkel (1942)
   Singer
6. John Philip Sousa (1854)
   Composer of marches
7. Marie Curie (1867)
   Scientist who discovered radium (radiation)
8. Edmond Halley (1656)
   Astronomer after whom the comet is named
9. Katherine Hepburn (1909)
   Actress
10. Richard Burton (1925)
    Actor
11. Fyodor Dostoyevsky (1821)
    Russian novelist
12. Grace Kelly (1929)
    Actress
13. Robert Louis Stevenson (1850)
    Novelist
14. Claude Monet (1840)
    French painter
15. Daniel Barenboim (1942)
    Orchestral conductor
16. Tiberius (42BC)
    Roman emperor
17. Martin Scorsese (1942)
    Film director
18. Alec Issigonis (1906)
    Car designer who created the Morris Minor and the Mini
19. Jodie Foster (1962)
    Actress
20. Samuel Cunard (1787)
    Shipping magnate
21. Voltaire (1694)
    French philosopher and writer
22. Billie Jean King (1943)
    Tennis champion
23. William Bonney (Billy the Kid) (1859)
    American outlaw
24. Toulouse-Lautrec (1864)
    French painter
25. Karl Benz (1844)
    Pioneer car manufacturer
26. Tina Turner (1939)
    Singer
27. Jimi Hendrix (1942)
    Rock guitarist
28. William Blake (1767)
    English poet and visionary
29. Louisa M. Alcott (1832)
    Novelist ('Little Women')
30. Winston Churchill (1874)
    British Prime Minister

December

1. Woody Allen (1935)
   Film actor and director
2. Maria Callas (1923)
   Opera singer
3. Walt Disney (1901)
   Film animator and producer
4. Jeff Bridges (1949)
   Actor
5. General Custer (1839)
   American cavalry commander
6. Dave Brubeck (1920)
   Jazz musician
7. Bernini (1598)
   Italian sculptor
8. Sammy Davis Jr (1925)
   American entertainer
9. Clarence Birdseye (1886)
   Pioneer of frozen food
10. Emily Dickinson (1830)
    American poet
11. Aleksandr Solzhenitsyn (1928)
    Russian novelist
12. Frank Sinatra (1915)
    Singer and actor
13. Dick Van Dyke (1925)
    Comedy actor
14. Nostradamus (1503)
    Astronomer who predicted the future
15. Alexandre-Gustave Eiffel (1832)
    Engineer who built the tower in Paris
16. Jane Austen (1775)
    Novelist
17. Humphry Davy (1778)
    Inventor of the miner's safety lamp
18. Steven Spielberg (1947)
    Film director and producer
19. Edith Piaf (1915)
    Singer
20. Jenny Agutter (1952)
    Actress
21. Jane Fonda (1937)
    Actress
22. Maurice and Robin Gibb (1949)
    Singers (The Bee Gees)
23. Richard Arkwright (1732)
    Inventor of wool-spinning machines
24. Kit Carson (1809)
    American frontiersman
25. Humphrey Bogart (1889)
    Actor
26. Phil Spector (1940)
    Songwriter and record producer
27. Louis Pasteur (1822)
    French chemist who invented vaccination
28. Maggie Smith (1934)
    Actress
29. Mary Tyler Moore (1937)
    Actress
30. Rudyard Kipling (1865)
    Novelist and poet
31. Anthony Hopkins (1937)
    Actor

There's nothing wrong with getting older. . .

I just wouldn't want it to happen to me!

SO, GARFIELD, YOU'RE GOING TO BE FOURTEEN THIS WEEK, HUH?

THANK YOU FOR REMINDING ME

FOUR-TEEN... WOW-WEE. FOURTEEN, FOURTEEN, FOURTEEN. FOUUUUUUUR-TEEEEEEN

A TEENSE SENSITIVE, ARE WE?

JIM DAVIS 6-15

MOM MADE YOU A TIE FOR YOUR BIRTHDAY, GARFIELD

A TIE?!

OH WELL, I GUESS IT'S THE THOUGHT THAT COUNTS

AND THESE CUFF LINKS

I MUST REMEMBER TO SEND HER A THANK-YOU BOMB

JIM DAVIS 6-16

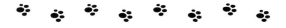

JIM DAVIS 6-17

HAPPY BIRTHDAY, GARFIELD!

BY THE WAY, MAY I BORROW YOUR GOLF CLUBS?

SURE

RIGHT AFTER I'M FINISHED WITH THEM!

60

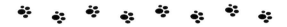